BARNES
&NOBLE
BOOKS

NEW YORK

CLOUDS

PHOTOGRAPHS BY
PEKKA PARVIAINEN

TEXT BY
HENRY FOUNTAIN

CLOUDS

For information contact:
Barnes & Noble
122 Fifth Avenue
New York, NY 10011
212 633-4000

Barnes & Noble and colophon are
registered trademarks.

Publisher: Barbara J. Morgan
   Design: Richard J. Berenson
           Berenson Design & Books, Ltd.,
           New York, NY
Production: Della R. Mancuso
           Mancuso Associates, Inc.,
           North Salem, NY

Library of Congress Cataloging-in-Publication
Data is available on request.

ISBN 0-7607-5635-X

Printed in Singapore

First Printing

CONTENTS

A WORLD OF CLOUDS

I F YOU EVER GET TO THINKING that the earth is a dull and unchanging place, do yourself a favor: glance at the sky.

There's another world directly over your head, one that reveals an ever-shifting landscape. White balls of cotton lingering over a meadow on a summer afternoon. Vast sheets of gray moving in from across a lake. Delicate wisps of white soaring high above a mountaintop.

This is the world of clouds. It's a place of downy white cumulus and towering storm cells, of iridescent sheen and dense sea smoke, of rain, snow, hail, and lightning.

Mostly, though, it's a place of change. A cloud that arises in the afternoon can be gone by evening. Storm clouds that scud in to ruin a day can just as quickly scud off, leaving a sparkling night sky. No two cloudscapes are ever the same. Even a dreary blanket of low clouds— the kind that seems to hang around for days—can be a crazy quilt.

At its most basic, the world of clouds is a world of water. Tiny jots of H_2O, practically invisible and light

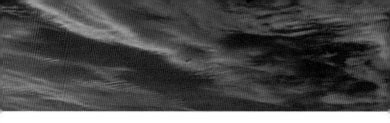

enough to float, are brought together by the trillions to form clouds.

What brings them together is the basic atmospheric processes: warming and cooling. Heat some air and it will rise. Cool it off and the water vapor in it will condense to droplets, forming a cloud. Cool it some more and the droplets may turn to ice crystals. Then mix in more rising and falling air and chances are you'll get rain or snow.

But that's just one type of cloud. There are many more—about a dozen main types, and many variations between.

This book is a handy guide to many of them, a Baedeker for the world of clouds and some of the optical effects they cause. You'll see some cloud formations that look familiar, but others that you'll rarely, if ever, encounter.

With his breathtaking images, master photographer Pekka Parviainen has done the work for you. You don't have to glance skyward. But if this book inspires you to do that, so much the better.

—Henry Fountain

THE CLASSIC puffy clouds of a picture-perfect day are of the cumulus family. **Fair-weather cumulus** often form on summer afternoons when the ground is heated by the sun, causing warm air to rise and the water vapor within it to condense. With their flat bottoms and fluffy tops, fair-weather cumulus are fairly innocuous, but as the air continues to rise, cumulus can become more threatening. **Swelling cumulus** can form in air that rises due to more intense heating of the ground, but they can also be created when an air mass hits an obstacle like a mountainside and is forced higher. Swelling cumulus can be towering masses of water droplets thousands of feet high. As heating and rising continue and smaller clouds come together, **cumulus congestive** form. These are massive towers that can measure 20,000 feet from top to bottom. The tops of these clouds remain relatively warm, however, so ice crystals do not form.

CUMULUS

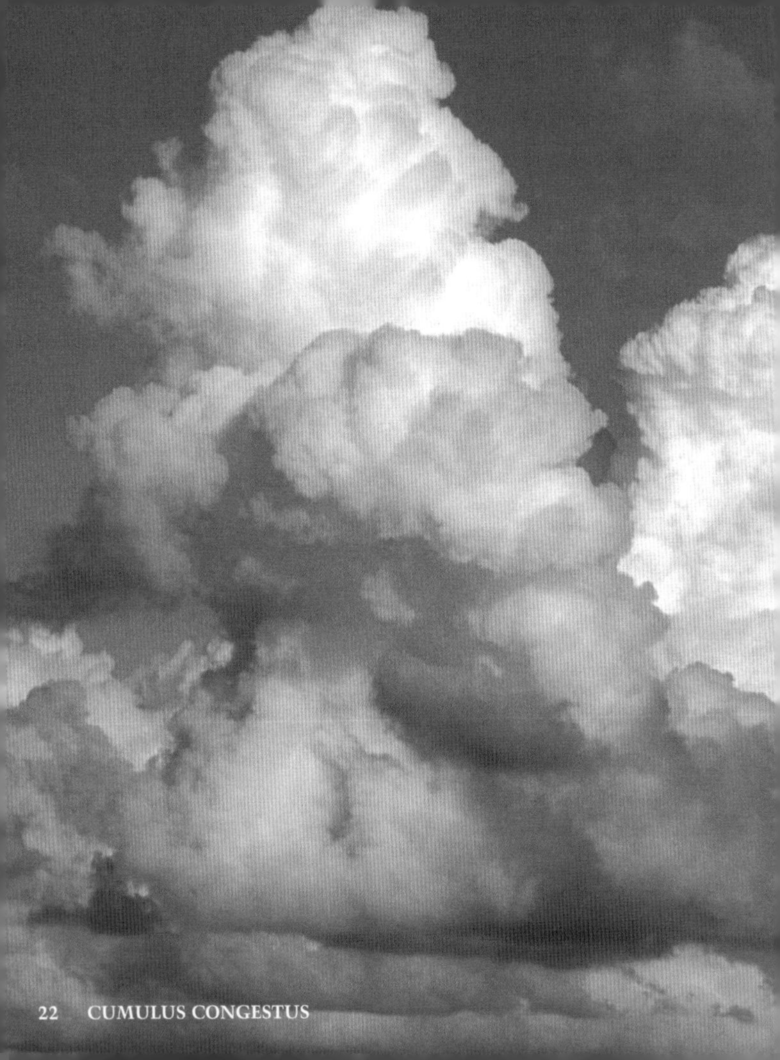

 CUMULUS CONGESTUS

STRATUS ARE LAYERED, featureless clouds that occur in stable air, forming a dull blanket that can appear thin and benign or thick and threatening. Stratus can take several forms, depending on where the stable air is. **Ground fog,** for example, is earthbound stratus; it forms when surface air cools overnight and water droplets condense. **Advection fog** often forms in the spring when warm, moist air blows over cool water. This is the kind of fog that "rolls in" along coastlines. If weak air currents push a layer of air slightly upward, cooling it to the point of condensation, **low stratus** are formed. These seldom lead to heavy rains, but can produce a steady, dismal drizzle. A ground fog that rises is another form of low stratus. Layers that form even higher up, to about 18,000 feet, are **altostratus;** when these thicken, it's a good time to find the rain gear. The highest layered clouds, **cirrostratus,** are thin and made up of ice crystals.

STRATUS

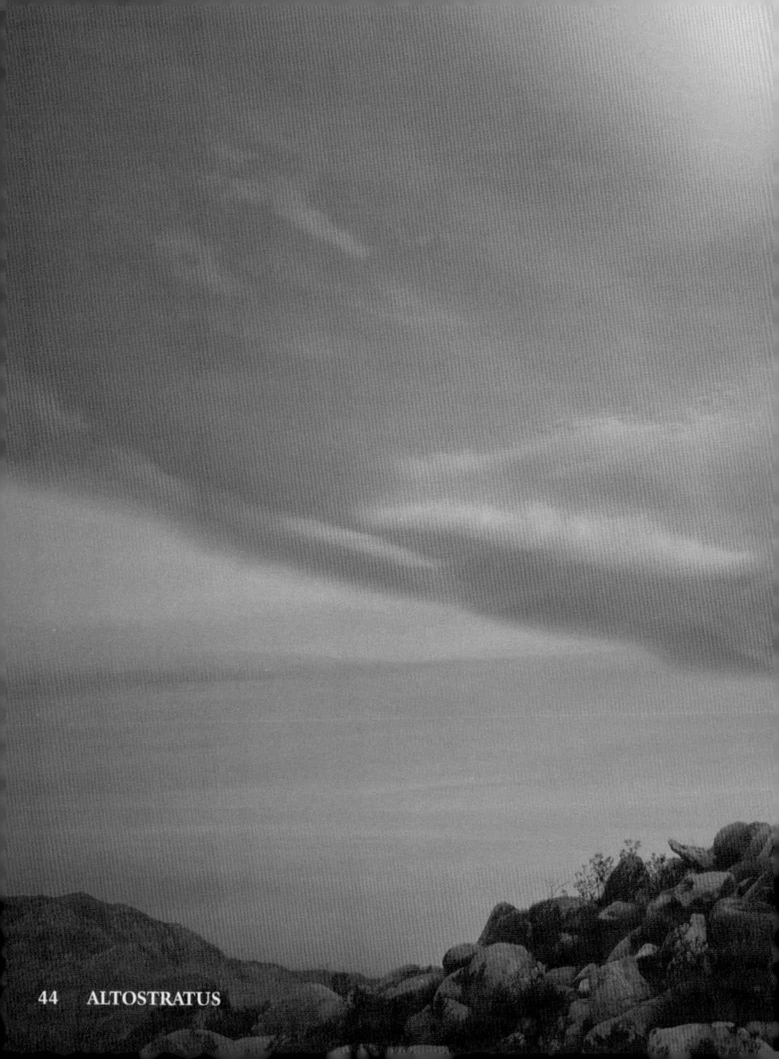

I N A PERFECT WORLD, puffy clouds would be one thing and layered clouds another, and the two would never mix. But the world is far from perfect, and many cloud formations are of an intermediate type, blending the puffballs of cumulus that rise on currents of warm air with the blankets of stratus that form in stable air. The lowest of these hybrids, **stratocumulus,** can have a lumpy, layered look, with breaks of clear sky between the lumps. **Altostratocumulus** have the same appearance of curds separated by clear air (creating what is sometimes called a buttermilk sky) but are higher, reaching 14,000 feet. With **altocumulus** the air is even more unstable, the rising air creating so many cloud lumps (called convective cells) that the sky takes on a rippled appearance. **Cirrocumulus** are higher still, but thinner, with smaller convective cells that form a dimpled layer, one that the sun has no difficulty peeking through.

CUMULUS
AND
STRATUS

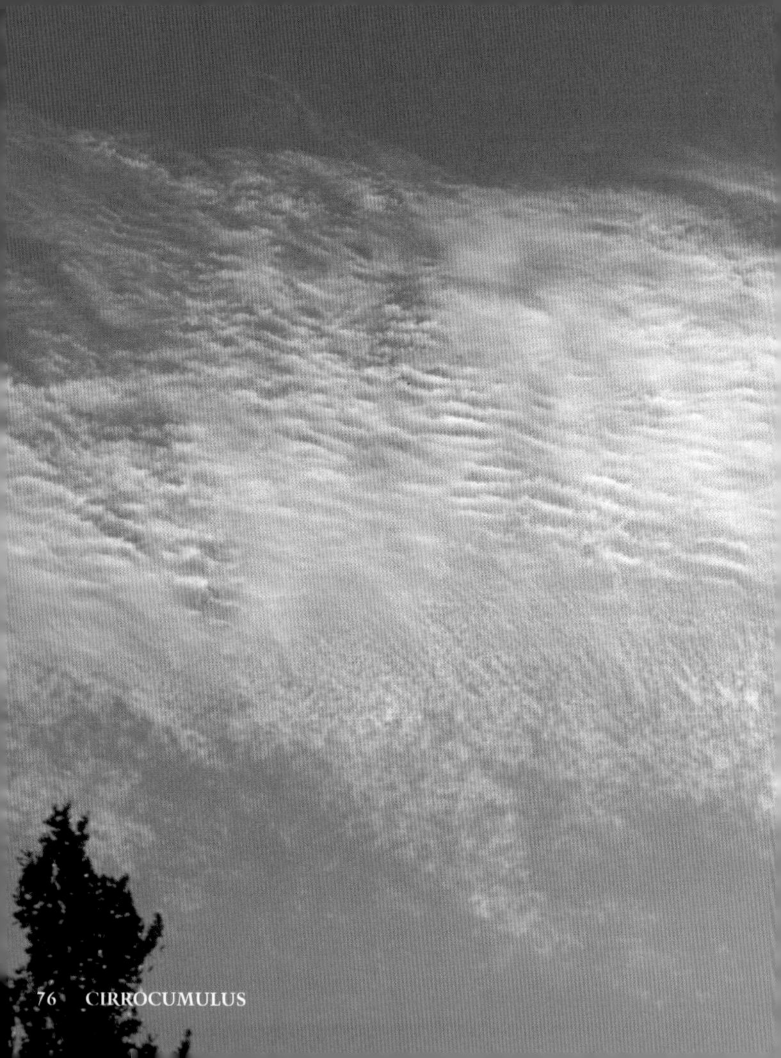

MOST RAIN AND SNOW comes from just two varieties of clouds, and depending on the type, it's easy to forecast the duration of the storm. **Cumulonimbus** are the great thunderheads, often with anvil-shaped tops, that can reach tens of thousands of feet into the sky. They are so tall that the tops freeze into ice crystals, and strong up- and downdrafts occur that can create hail. Mostly, though, cumulonimbus bring short, torrential downpours, often accompanied by lightning. Longer, soaking rains are the work of **nimbostratus,** which are created when a cold front meets a warm front. The cold air rides up and over the warm, condensing into a layer of clouds that hold a lot of moisture—and steadily let go of it, in the form of raindrops or snowflakes. A third type of precipitating cloud, **cirrus,** are high and delicately thin. While cirrus produce precipitation, usually in the form of ice crystals, the precipitation almost never reaches the ground, evaporating in midair.

PRECIPITATING

95

WITH RAIN comes one of the grandest of nature's optical effects, the rainbow. Rainbows occur during showers when the sun is behind the viewer, but rainbows can also easily be seen in the mists from fountains, waterfalls, and even lawn sprinklers. The sunlight is refracted, or bent, by the water droplets, separating into a spectrum from violet to red. This colored light then reflects off the back of the droplet toward the viewer. Incidental reflections can create a secondary rainbow that is usually dimmer than the first. Depending upon the position of the sun, the rainbow can form a full arc high in the sky or a lesser one close to the ground. The color of the background sky goes a long way toward determining whether the bow is a striking, almost garish display or a softer one in muted tones.

RAINBOW

BILLOWS OCCUR among altocumulus, cirrocumulus, and other high clouds, and are caused by layers of wind of varying speed above and below the cloud level. The difference in wind speed creates a shearing action, rolling the clouds into long, parallel strands or corn rows, sometimes with troughs of clear air between them. Billow clouds are a warning to pilots to steer clear, for the same shearing forces that shape the clouds can have a devastating effect on an airplane, or at least make for a harrowing, bumpy ride.

BILLOWS

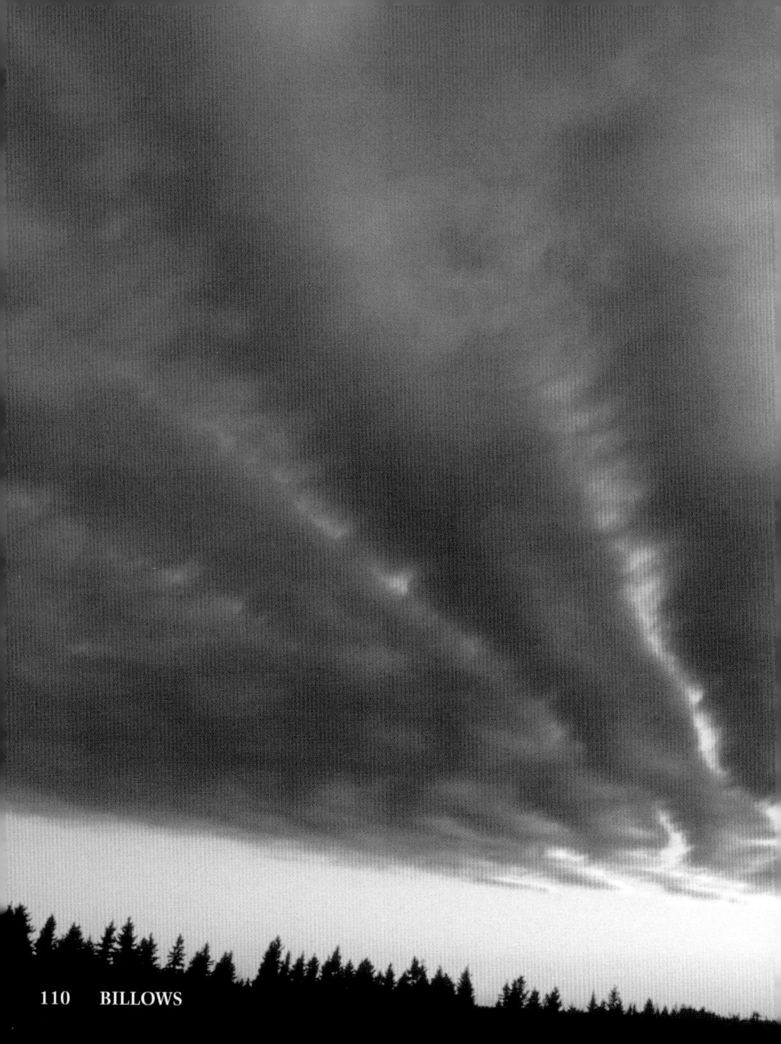

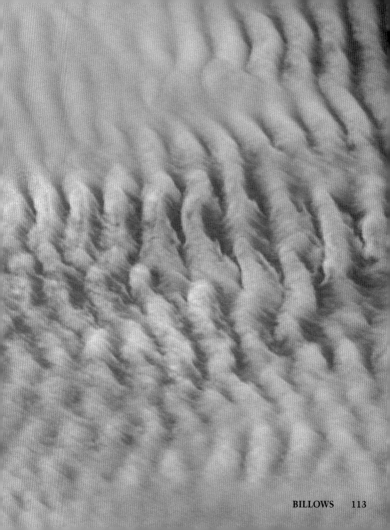

114

As THE NAME IMPLIES, lenticular clouds are lens shaped, and are formed when fast-moving air passes over a mountainside or other rugged feature of the landscape. As a result of the flow, the more stable air on the lee side of the mountain tends to rise and fall in a wave. Lenticular clouds form at the peak of this wave and can often occur in layers, like a stack of pancakes. Despite the movement of air above them, the clouds remain stationary and their edges distinct. To some people their shape resembles flying saucers, and lenticular formations have sometimes been the inspiration for reports of alien invasions. More accurately, they can serve as a forewarning of an invading snowstorm.

LENTICULAR

IF LENTICULAR CLOUDS are relatively rare, then the particular type of lenticular cloud called a cap is rarer still. A cap cloud forms on top of a mountain rather than on its leeward side, when air is forced up by the mountain and cools. The cap may appear to stream up and over the summit and back down the other side. Some mountains appear to have a permanent cap, but in those cases the cloud is likely to be continually forming and dissipating as more air moves in.

CAP

IF A CUMULUS CLOUD gets big enough and rises high enough, it can develop a cap of its own, called a pileus. The process of formation is roughly the same as for a cap cloud on a mountaintop, with the big cloud—often a massive cumulus congestive formation—acting as an obstacle and forcing a mass of warm, moist air to rise above it. The warm air cools, the water vapor in it condenses to droplets, and a cap cloud forms. Clouds that form all at once like this often have droplets of uniform size, so pileus clouds can display a strong iridescence when they refract and split sunlight. The show won't last forever, however—eventually the cumulus will rise more and pierce the pileus, its remnants forming a collar or skirt.

PILEUS

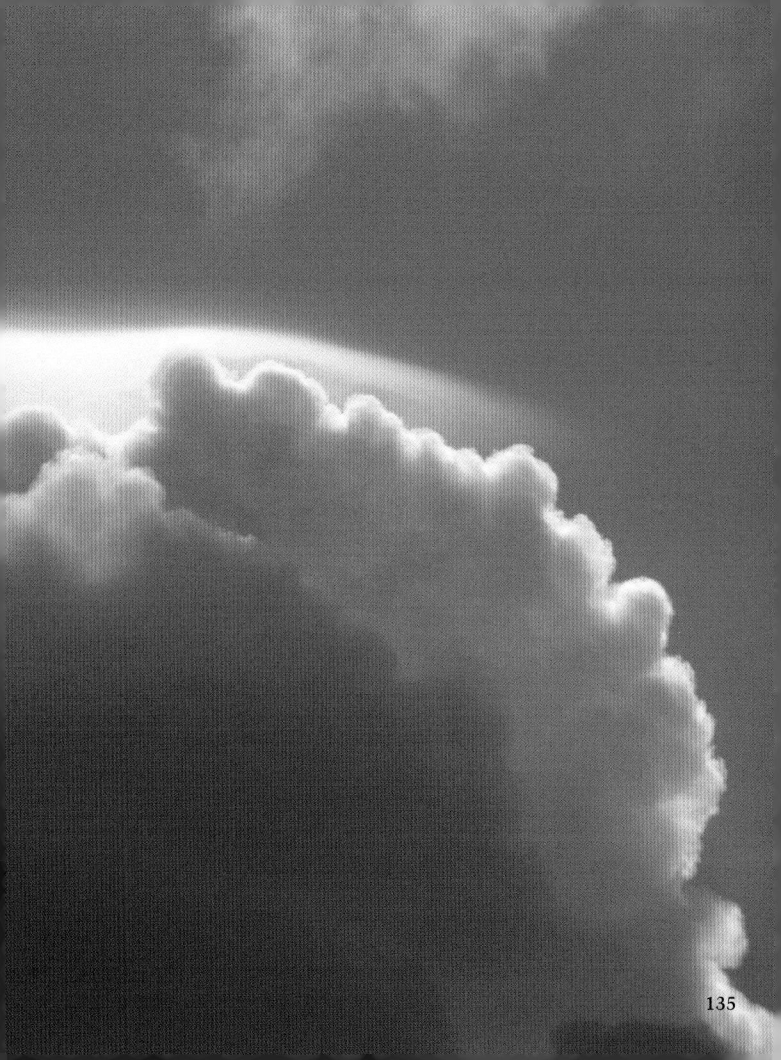

WHISPER-THIN noctilucent clouds are extremely uncommon and form in the rarefied air of the mesopause, at 250,000 to 300,000 feet. They are the highest clouds on earth, far higher than cirrus, which they are sometimes mistaken for. Noctilucent clouds appear only in high latitudes and only in summer, and are so delicate they can be seen only at twilight, when the sun has set on all but the high reaches of the atmosphere. They take their name from their shimmering appearance in the darkening sky. They are most likely made up of ice crystals, although scientists are not sure how they form.

NOCTILUCENT

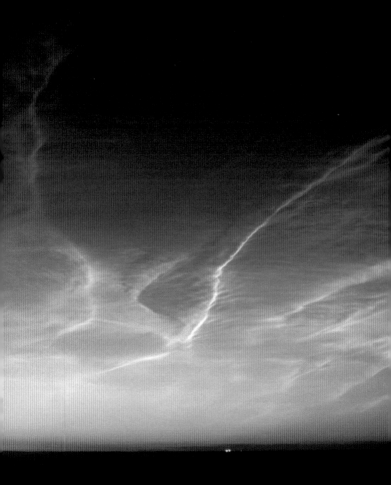

141

147

ANOTHER RARE high cloud type is the nacreous cloud, also known as the mother-of-pearl cloud, which shines with an iridescent quality when it refracts the sun's rays at twilight. Nacreous clouds form in the stratosphere between 50,000 and 100,000 feet. In some ways they are the high-altitude equivalent of lenticular clouds, forming when strong, high winds pass over a mountain range and create a wave of uplift on the lee side. The ash and dust spewed by volcanoes is thought to spur the creation of these clouds by providing the nuclei for ice crystals to form. Following the 1991 eruption of Mount Pinatubo in the Philippines, for example, there were many reports of nacreous clouds.

NACREOUS

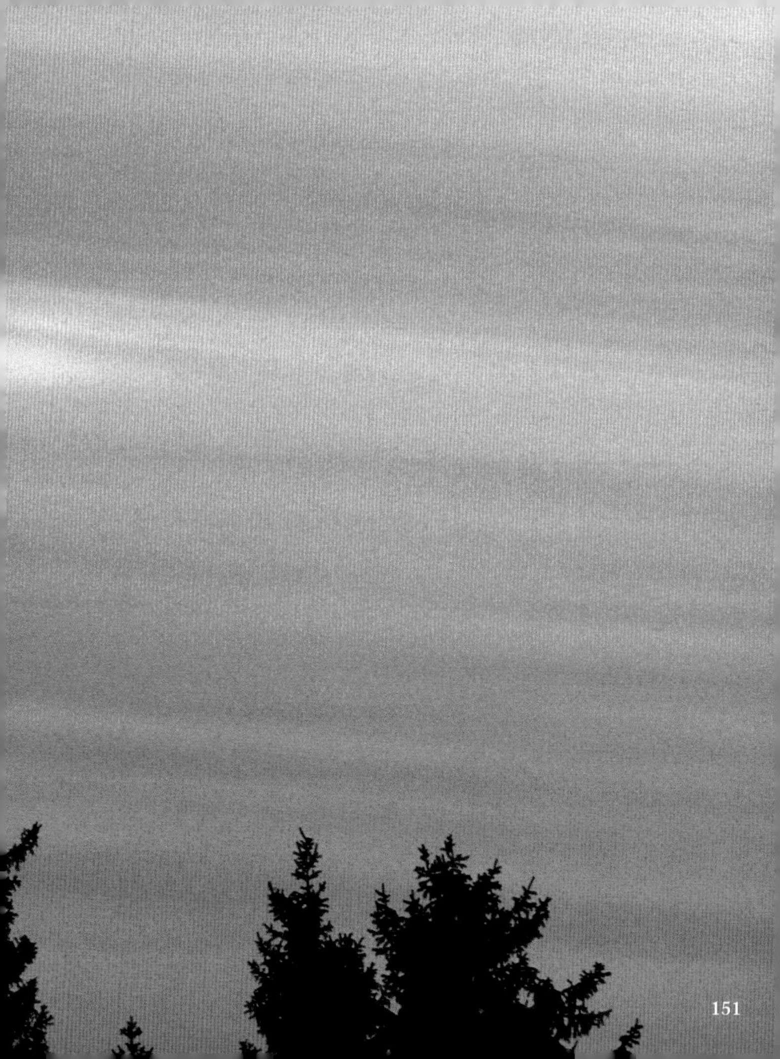

SHORT FOR CONDENSATION TRAILS, a contrail is a cloud created by the exhaust of a jet airplane. That exhaust contains water vapor, which when it hits cold low-pressure air at cruising altitude, 30,000 to 40,000 feet, immediately condenses into droplets. The process is similar to what happens when you exhale on a cold day and "see" your breath. If the upper atmosphere is very dry, a contrail may not last long. But if the atmosphere is more humid, then the trail will linger and the wind will take over, broadening the contrail's thin line or creating cirruslike wisps perpendicular to the trail's axis. Scientists are finding increasing evidence that in certain parts of the world where there is a large amount of jet travel, contrails can affect weather patterns by blocking and reflecting sunlight.

CONTRAILS

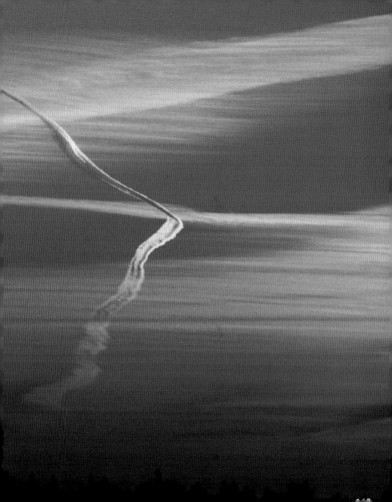

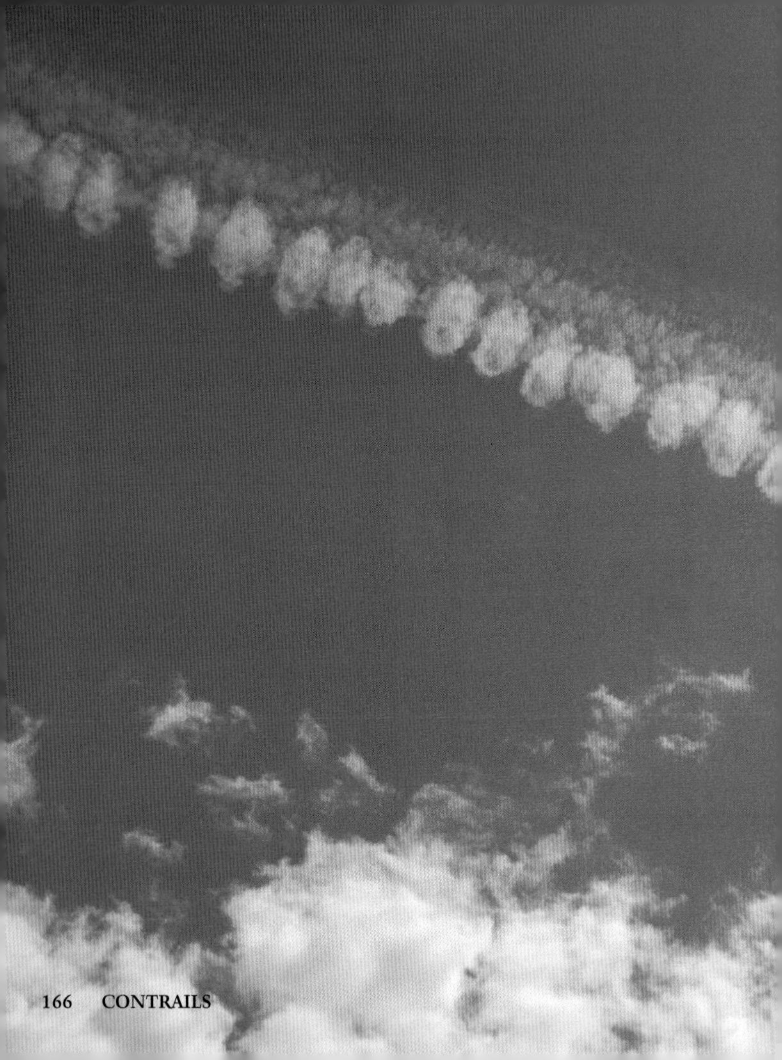

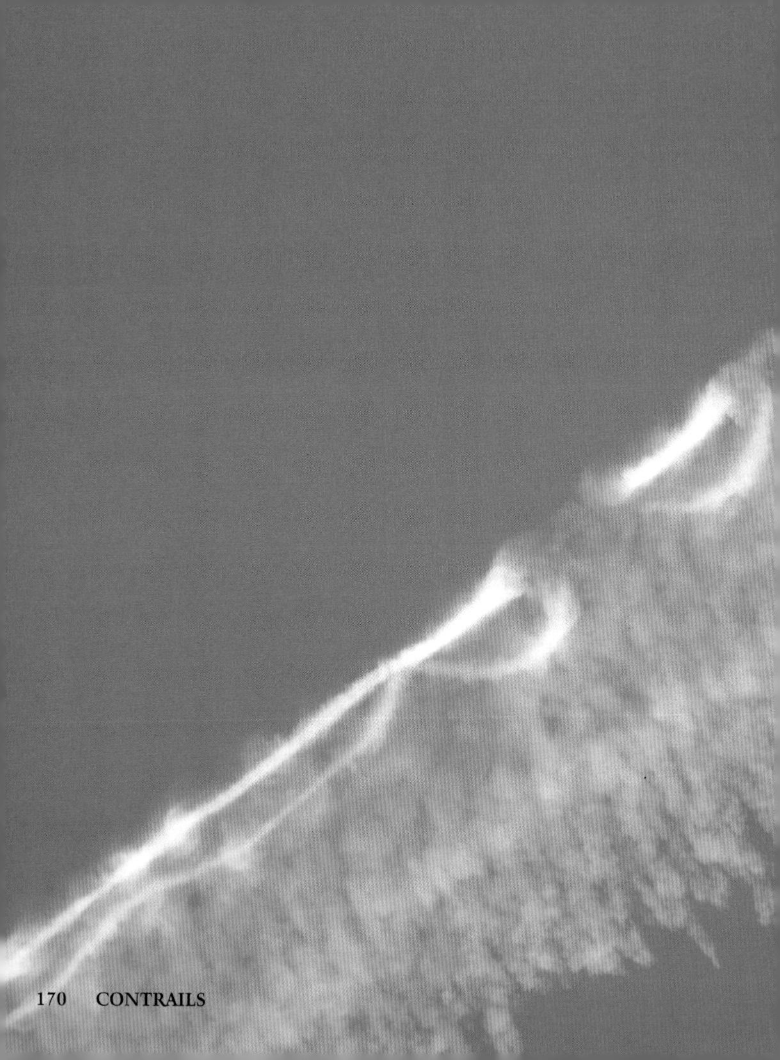

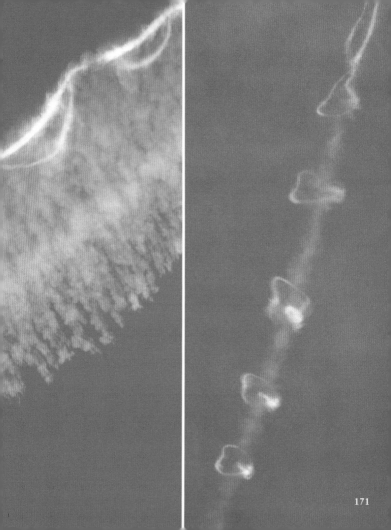

RY RAIN. That may sound like an oxymoron, but when rain or snow falls into dry air, it can evaporate before it hits the ground. The effect, called virga, occurs most often in the winter, when air is coldest and therefore cannot hold much moisture. You can't feel virga, of course, but you can often see it—it may appear as vertical wisps or streaks trailing from midlevel cumulus clouds. At the altitude of the clouds, conditions are right to create rain or snow, but as the drops or flakes fall, they hit much drier air and vanish, becoming water vapor once again.

VIRGA

179

WHEN A WARM, light air mass lies atop a dense, colder one and the two are moving at different speeds, the boundary between them can become unstable, with eddies starting to appear. Over time, the eddies can develop into a type of billow cloud that resembles a cresting wave. The effect is due to the shearing forces between the moving air masses, and the result is Kelvin-Helmholtz instability. It's not surprising that the clouds look like waves, because the same shearing forces—though between wind and water—create ripples on the ocean's surface. In fact, the Kelvin-Helmholtz instability can occur anywhere there are two layers of different density traveling at different speeds—even on Jupiter, where the effect creates the planet's swirling pattern of gases.

KELVIN-
HELMHOLTZ

THE SOFT, sculptured clouds called mammatus are a rare example of a cloud that is formed by sinking, rather than rising, air. When they appear on the undersides of storm clouds, they are usually a sign that the bad weather has passed. The air is still unstable, with lingering up- and downdrafts of the kind that create rain, but the ice crystals at the top of the storm cloud— often a massive cumulonimbus that has spread out into an anvil shape—have started to fall, cooling the air below. The result is an expanse of pouchlike structures that appear to hang off the storm cloud. Depending on the time of day and the amount of sunlight, mammatus can range in color from an ominous gray-green to a more playful orange or pink.

MAMMATUS

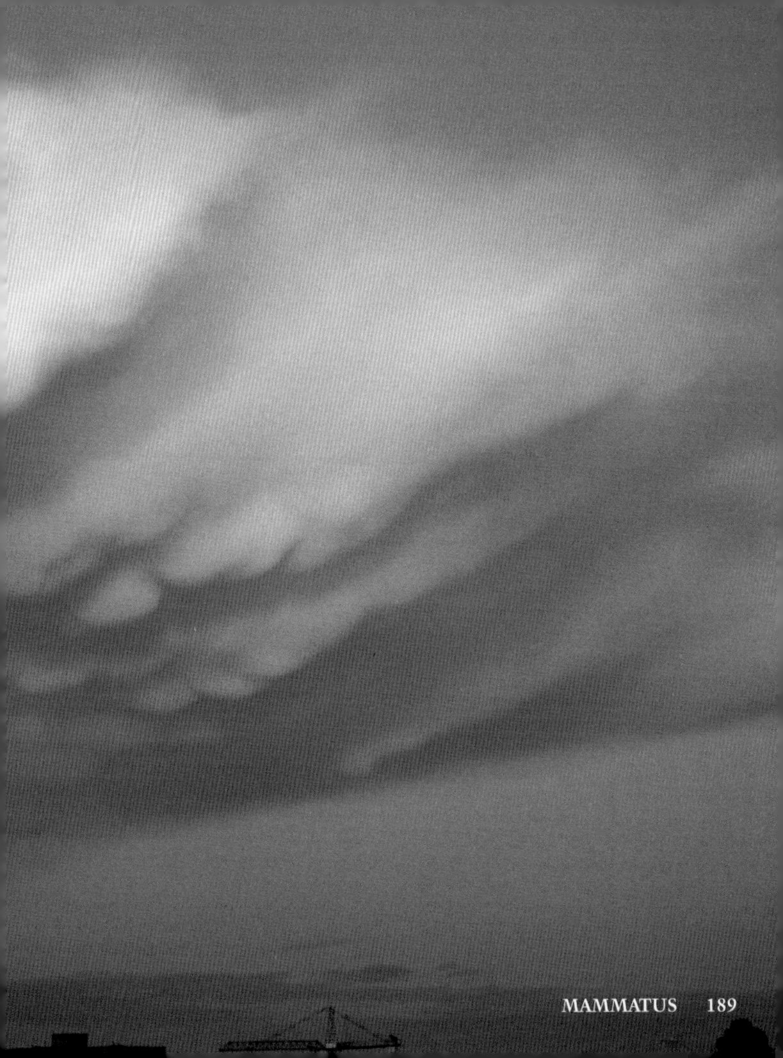

WHEN VERY COLD AIR drifts across warmer water, some of the water evaporates and rapidly condenses into droplets, forming the intermittent fog known as sea smoke. It can consist of wisps of cloud or denser patches alternating with clear areas, and it can be beautiful, making a bay or other harbor seem like a slow-simmering cauldron. But beneath sea smoke's beauty lies danger. Mariners who would proceed cautiously in a dense fog bank may be lured into a sense of complacency by sea smoke's patchwork nature, but even a small wisp of cloud can hide a boat or other hazard.

SEA SMOKE

A FUNNEL CLOUD—sometimes called a land spout or, on the ocean, a water spout—is a twisting mass of water droplets, formed when unstable air in a large cumulus cloud begins to spin. Air is drawn into the middle of this vortex, cools because of the low pressure, gains humidity, and then condenses, forming a spinning tendril that extends toward the surface from the larger cloud above. By definition, though, a funnel cloud doesn't reach the ground. If it does, it is considered a tornado, and soon the water droplets are joined by dust and debris as the high-spinning winds wreak their destruction.

FUNNEL

ICE CRYSTALS can affect light differently than water droplets, their hexagonal structure reflecting and refracting it with precision. A **sun halo,** for example, occurs when light is refracted by the ice crystals in high clouds like cirrostratus; halos can often be seen on cold winter days, with moon halos on winter nights. The most common type of halo is 22 degrees of arc from the sun, as that is how much the hexagonal crystals bend the light. The halo is a complete circle because the ice crystals are floating in a random jumble; when the crystals align horizontally, as can happen when they are closer to the ground and falling, **parhelia,** or **sun dogs,** can be seen. These consist of bright spots of color at 22 degrees on either side of the sun. A third ice effect, the **sun pillar,** can be seen at sunrise or sunset, when the low sun reflects off the face of ice crystals in high clouds.

ICE EFFECTS

223

CLOUDS DON'T TAKE ON COLOR only at sunrise and sunset. Given the proper conditions, a cloud can assume an iridescent sheen, called irisation, at any time of day. Generally, the cloud must be high and thin—a wispy layer of altostratus is a good candidate— and the water droplets within it must be of fairly uniform size. Those droplets refract light, bending it like a prism and separating it into its rainbow of colors. When the droplet sizes vary and the amount of bending varies, the colors tend to wash out into white. But when the droplets are nearly the same size, they concentrate the colors and create a pastel iridescence at the cloud's edges, like mother-of-pearl.

IRISATION

227

WHEN A THIN LAYER of high clouds lightly shrouds the sun or moon, chances are a corona will be visible. Think of a corona as a circular rainbow of small diameter, caused by the light from the sun or moon being refracted by the water droplets in the cloud. This refraction creates concentric rings of color, ranging from violet-blue at the innermost ring to red at the outermost.

The effect can also be seen in a sky that may be cloudless but carries a large amount of pollen, as in forested areas during certain times of the year. The pollen grains refract light just as water droplets do, but because of the shape of the grains, the resulting **pollen corona** can be elliptical or contain a symmetrical pattern of bright areas.

CORONA

CREPUSCULAR RAYS occur at the beginning or end of the day, when the low sun is partially obscured by the sawtooth edges of thick clouds, mountain peaks, or some other irregular feature of the landscape. The light that makes it past the obstructions is scattered by haze or dust in the atmosphere, giving the effect of rays that, due to the viewer's perspective, appear to radiate in a fan shape from the sun's location, called the solar point. When combined with the reddening of the sky at sunset or sunup, the effect can be spectacular.

Those who spot crepuscular rays can double their enjoyment by turning around and looking in the opposite direction. If conditions are right, anti-crepuscular rays may be visible—shafts of scattered light that seem to converge on a spot that is 180 degrees from the sun, what is known as the antisolar point. If the sun is above the horizon, then the antisolar point will be below it, so the anticrepuscular rays will disappear as they come together. As with crepuscular rays, the shafts of light are really parallel but appear to converge—just as parallel train tracks appear to intersect at some point in the distance.

CREPUSCULAR RAYS

THERE ARE many times other than sunrise or sunset when the sun's rays are visible. When the bright sun shines past the edges of a thick cloud and there is haze, dust, or the droplets of a far-off rain shower to scatter the light, sunbeams can be seen. If the cloud is high enough, the sunbeams may appear to radiate in all directions around the sky. If the cloud is thick enough—a swelling cumulus or cumulus congestive, perhaps—the backlighting from the sun may appear to give it a silver lining, its shimmering edges contrasting greatly with its dark gray or black underside.

SUNBEAMS

NATURE'S most spectacular nighttime light show is not a cloud at all. The aurora borealis, or northern lights, occurs when electrically charged particles interact with gases in the atmosphere. These particles, mostly electrons, are part of the solar wind that is constantly emitted by the sun. When the particles reach earth, they are attracted by our planet's magnetic field and accelerate toward the atmosphere, where they strike gas atoms and ionize them, creating brief bursts of colored light. The bursts of countless ionizing atoms can appear like a shimmering curtain or veil in the night sky. Because the magnetic field is at its strongest near the poles, the displays can usually be seen only in far northern or far southern latitudes (where the phenomenon is known as the aurora australis). But at times of extreme solar activity—when sunspots and flares cause the solar wind to become a gale—the northern lights can be seen in the continental United States.

AURORA
BOREALIS

273

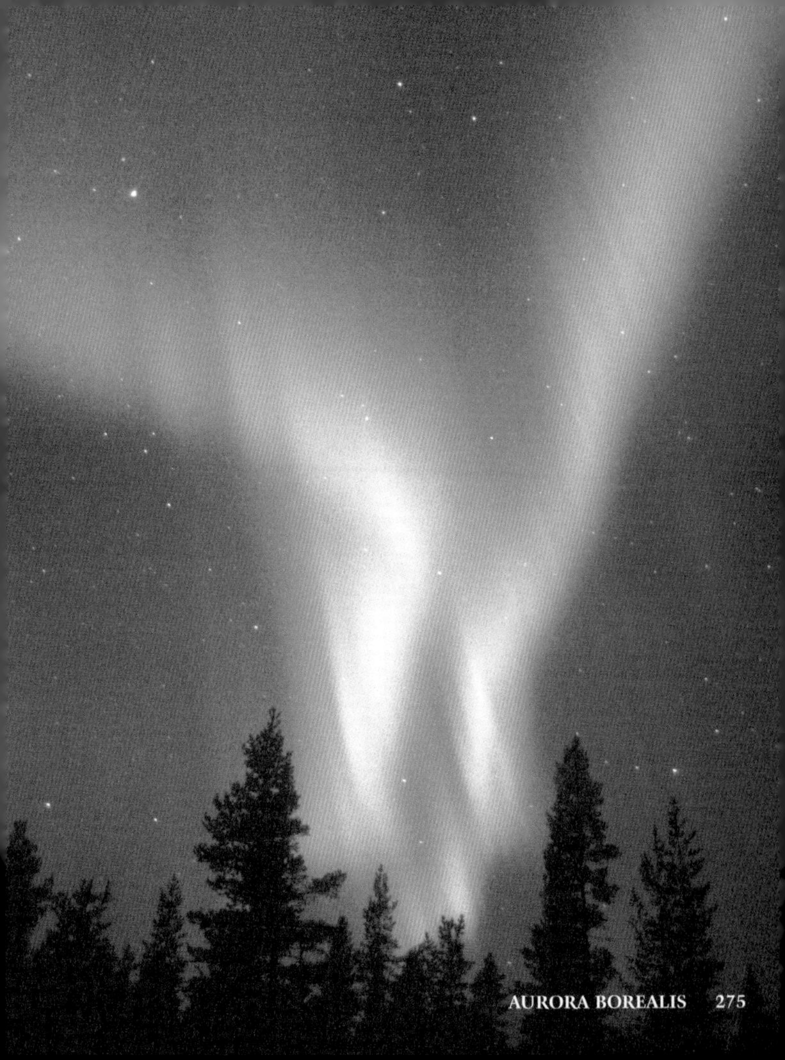

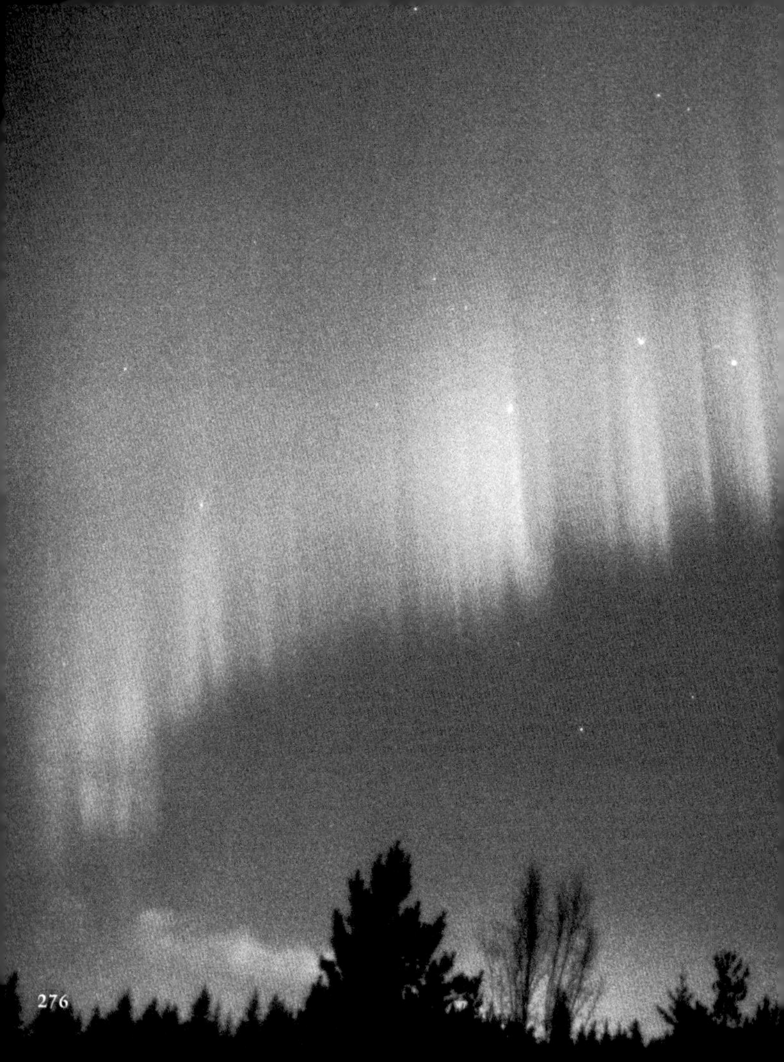

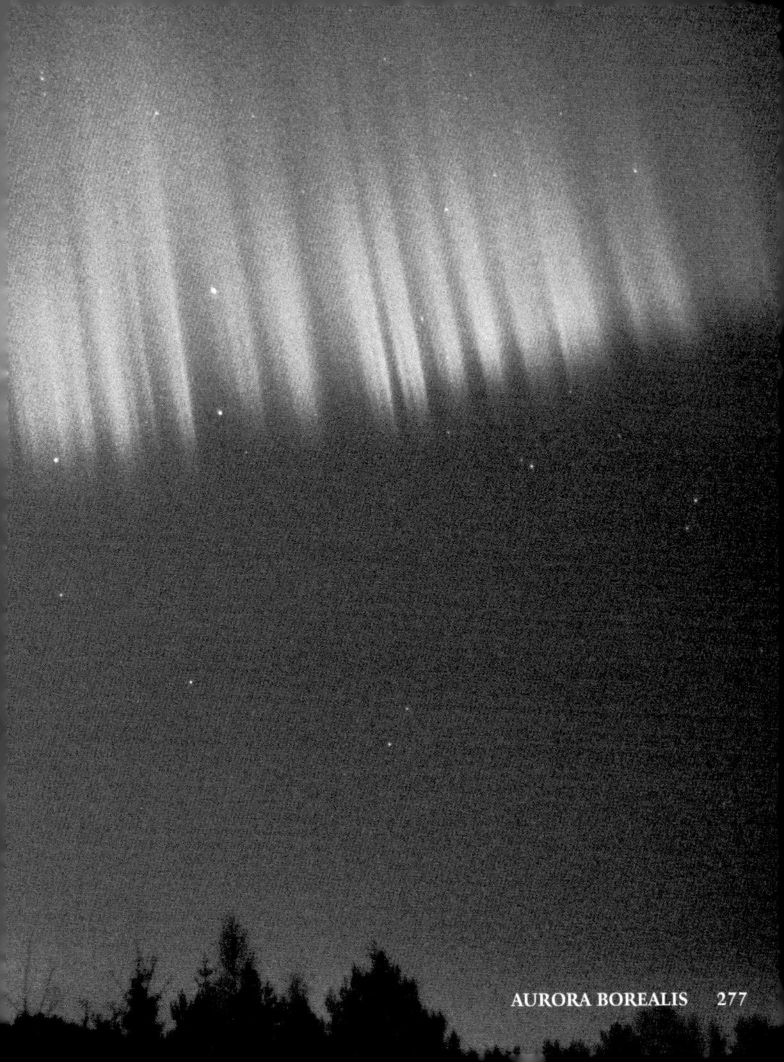

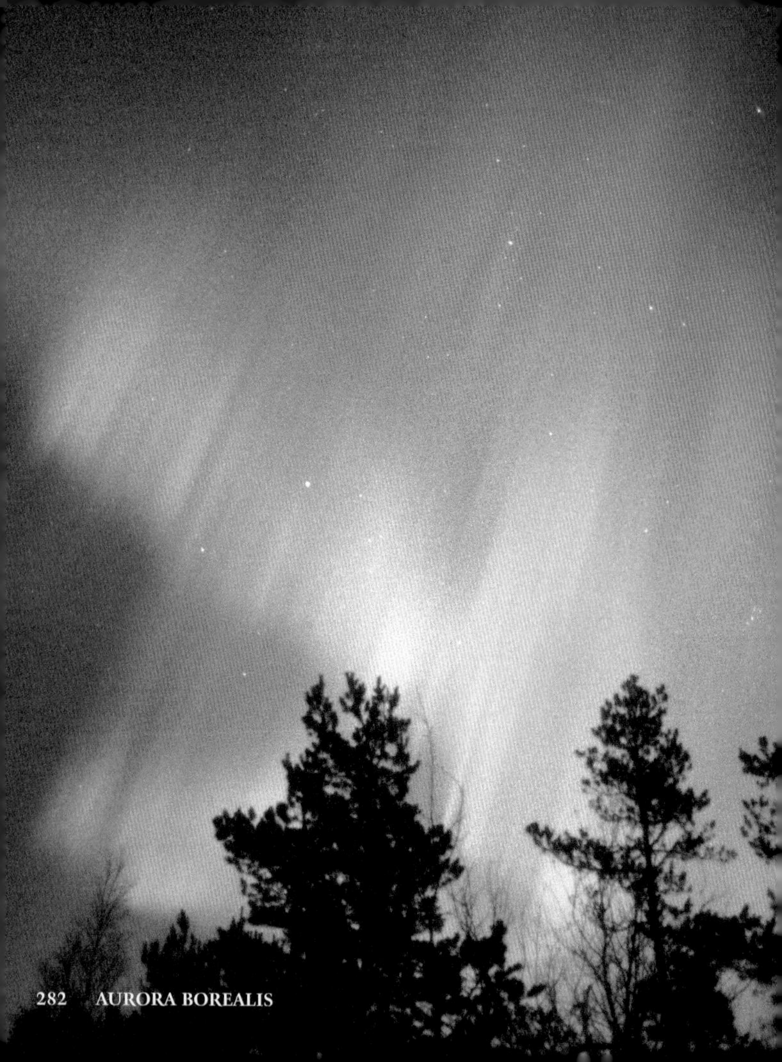

283

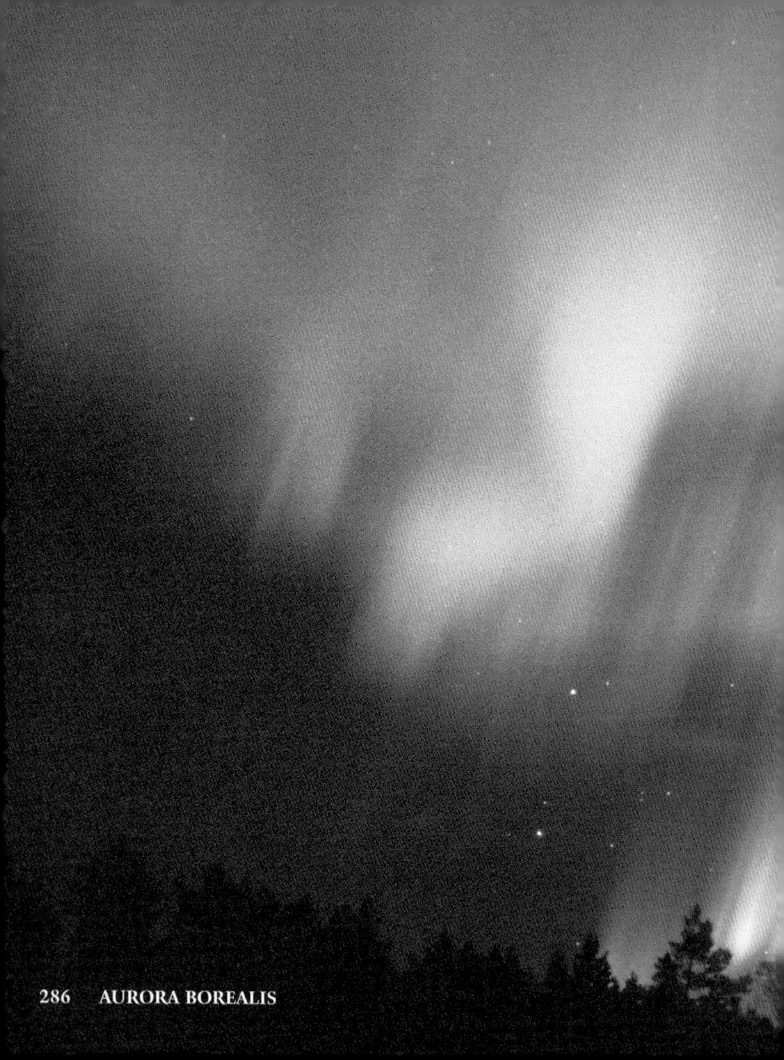

CERTAINLY MORE PEOPLE have talked about the green flash phenomenon than have actually seen it, since observing one requires good vision, extraordinarily clear skies and a flat, far-off horizon—the kind that can be found across an open sea. But lucky witnesses report seeing one or two seconds of emerald-green light as the last bit of the sun slips below the horizon. This is caused by the refraction of the setting sun's light by the atmosphere, coupled with a mirage effect that makes the green portion appear larger than it is. Green flashes can also be seen at dawn— but the observer has to know precisely where and when the sun is going to rise.

GREEN FLASH

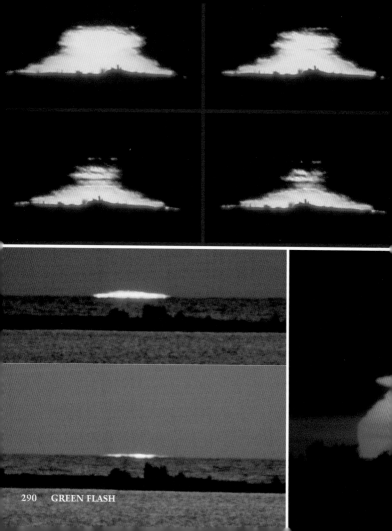

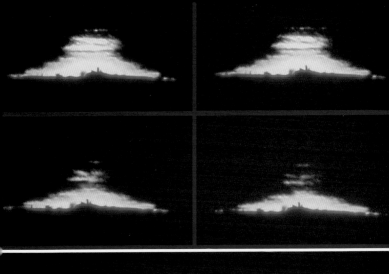

291

WHEN THE SUN IS LOW on the horizon, its light travels through much more atmosphere than when it is directly overhead. All that air—particularly the dust and dirt particles, water vapor, ice crystals, and aerosol pollutants it contains—scatters the shorter wavelengths that are a part of sunlight, leaving the longer violet, red, and orange wavelengths behind.

But that's only half the story. In order to make a spectacular morning or evening display, the light needs to reflect off something. In the most vivid sunrises and sunsets, nature obliges with high clouds, which seem to come ablaze as they catch the low sun's vibrant hues.

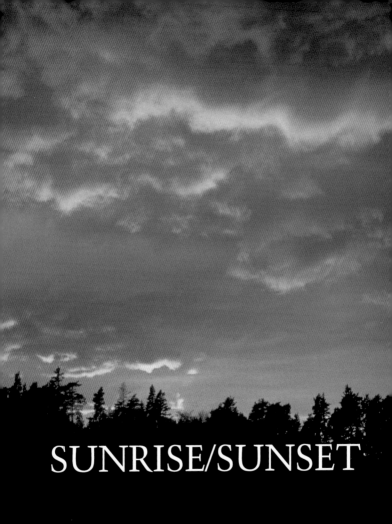

SUNRISE/SUNSET

A BOLT OF LIGHTNING can be a thing of beauty, but it's the type of beauty that is best appreciated from a safe distance. Lightning is a product of a thundercloud in which electrical charges have built up to the point where a current can travel through the air, ionizing the gas and creating a flash of light. Lightning can occur within a cloud if there are areas of positive and negative charge, between a negative area in one cloud and a positive area in another, or between a cloud and the ground. The long streaks of cloud-to-ground lightning are often the most awe inspiring—and the most dangerous—since they contain enough energy to light up the whole neighborhood.

LIGHTNING